The Amazing Adventures of Bing

The Parachuting Dog – A True Story

By Gil Boyd BEM

Published by
Impressions Publishing
Tel: 01487 843311
www.printandpublish.co.uk

First Edition published 2012
© Gil Boyd BEM 2012

Printed and bound in Great Britain
Impressions Print And Publish

A catalogue record for this book
is available from The British Library
ISBN 978-1-908374-32-5

Dedication Page

The Author

Gil served in the 2nd Battalion The Parachute Regiment until 1974. On leaving, he joined the Royal Military Police (Territorial Army), where he attained the rank of WO1 RSM at Allied Rapid Reaction Corps, Germany, whilst serving for 30 years with the civilian Police Service.

He had various duties during that time which included, being a Police Diving Supervisor for the Underwater Search & Recovery Unit, and for the last 15 years as the Principal Technical Officer covering all aspects of technology for the Serious and Organised Crime Unit.

He has designed many innovative solutions still used by both the Police and the Army today and received numerous awards for his achievements including the prestigious BBC Television's Tomorrows World "Inventor of the Year" Award. He was responsible for inventing the first miniature microwave camera system worn by Police and Army search dogs called WOLVES (Wireless Operational Link & Video Exploration System) which locates people in dark and confined spaces.

Gil gained a lot of experience working with Police and Military dogs and used that knowledge to write this story through the eyes of the dog.

He is now a Trustee of the Airborne Assault Museum at Duxford where he shares his experiences with visitors to the museum and archive of The Parachute Regiment and Airborne Forces.

All the proceeds from this Book will be in aid of two charities, The Afghanistan Trust which supports the needs of injured Parachute Regiment personnel and their families, and also the Airborne Assault Museum at the Imperial War Museum, Duxford in Cambridgeshire which preserves the history of The Parachute Regiment and Airborne Forces.

CONTENTS

ACKNOWLEDGEMENTS

A special thanks to Rob Courtney who inspired me to put pen to paper with his initial idea of the book.

I would like to thank Jon Baker, the Curator, Becks Skinner, the Deputy Curator, and Harvey Grenville, the Editor of ParaData and all of the Airborne Assault Museum at Duxford for their tireless efforts there, and the information they have provided for making my life easier on the research for this book.

I would like to thank my wife Theodora for her total support of my work for The Parachute Regiment & Airborne Forces, and for the long hours she spent proof reading the finished manuscript.

My thanks go to Major General Sir Peter Downward KCVO, CB, DSO, DFC for his time, support and kindness in filling in so many missing pieces of how these brave dogs and their handlers operated behind enemy lines with his vast personal knowledge as their Platoon Commander during the Second World War.

To John Ward ex 16 Independent (Lincoln) Company The Parachute Regiment for the amazing pen and ink drawings he kindly produced for the book.

To all those that buy this book, who will not only read about this remarkable dog and his friends, but in so doing, assist the Afghanistan Trust with their work in supporting wounded soldiers and their families in the healing process for years to come.

To all a big thank you

Gil Boyd BEM

Foreword by Major General Sir Peter Downward KCVO, CB, DSO, DFC

A question I was often asked when recounting my days in the Parachute Regiment in the 1939-45 War was "What was the purpose of having trained parachute dogs?" The simple answer was to have extra eyes, extra ears and a sensitive nose to help soldiers on patrol at night.

Bing and his comrades were very much part of the Scout Platoon and often covered long distances on foot beside their handlers, including Corporal Bailey and Corporal Walton, and often under fire from the enemy.

My soldiers were all trained as snipers and their skills were put to the test in built-up areas such as Koesfeld and Osnabruck in searching for enemy snipers. Associated with the tension and stress of battle with inevitable casualties, all my soldiers loved our canine friends and would treat them as pets – often with a piece of chocolate or some tasty treat from their rations.

After the war in Europe, the 13th Parachute Battalion (still commanded by Lt Col Peter Luard) was posted to the Far East in readiness for operations against the Japanese. The dogs did not accompany us but were able to return to their original owners, or as my soldiers would refer to it as 'Blighty Leave'.

Many years after the 1939-45 War I decided that the Airborne

Museum, then at Aldershot, should have a model of Bing, and to this end I had him made up from several photographs by a professional modeller as a true replica of this brave boy with the Dickin Medal, He is now in the Airborne Assault Museum at the Imperial War Museum, Duxford.

Peter Downward.

9

Chapter 1 - Joining Up

"I look back now in my old age at the things which I so enjoyed, especially my time in the Army as a war dog where I met so many good friends................... I am tired now and need to rest"........ ....*I curled up and fell asleep and dreamt of my days as a war dog for a very special unit of The Parachute Regiment during the latter stages of the Second World War.*

"I knew my puppy days were over........... I looked up into the eyes of a tall well built man in uniform and heard him call me Bing for the very first time. I knew straight away that it was to be my new name, every word and command given to me from that moment, ended with the word Bing.

I had been named Brian before, when I was growing up with this kind lady called Betty Fetch, who knew I had special skills and volunteered me for service in the Army. I had heard on Betty's radio that we were at war with Germany, and there were reports on it daily. I did eat a lot of food as a big dog as I grew up, and times were hard for Betty with the rationing of food during this war; only the Army could support my needs.

As I left her, I saw her eyes were full of tears as she whispered in my ear, "Brian, I will see you soon; be careful".

I came to love my new name BING, and I responded as quickly as I could, as it was to be a new chapter of my life. I also felt I was going to get the same warmth and reassurance from this person in my life, as I had always had from Betty.

I was born in 1942, and I was the smallest of a litter of half Alsatian and half collie pups, so I was a bit of a mish mash. I never saw my brothers and sisters again when I joined the Army which at times was to make me sad and reflect on the love we all shared together.

Alsatian dogs were a breed of dogs originally from Germany, and brought to England a long time ago.

Here I was in 1944, a two year old dog with lots to offer and full of enthusiasm for my new position in the Army. My ears would prick up and my tail would swish from side to side uncontrollably when I heard my name called. How proud I was to have such a nice person call me his dog now. I instinctively held my head up high and listened so carefully to every word he spoke. I had one ear that used to droop at the tip, making me a special dog, because everybody recognised me straight away.

The young man that kept putting his arm around my neck and patting me on the head was called Ken Bailey, who was a corporal with two stripes on the sleeve of his army uniform. I knew we would be really close friends from then on, and that he would look after me. He was my handler and my new best friend.

Our first camp was to be an Army War Dog Training school near Potters Bar in a county called Hertfordshire. I was to see many counties and many countries before my service ended and this was the first one.

I had initial tests at this camp and passed them with flying colours. It lasted for two weeks, whereupon I became a fully qualified patrol dog which was the basic level of entry into the Army.

I knew as I progressed, that there were lots more challenges to face in the future, and Ken knew a lot about animals and was often called upon to help with other breeds of dogs. He gained his experience in the Royal Army Veterinary Corps which was the Army's hospital for all animals. If you got sick, they looked after you and made you better.

Ken had trained me well, but there was much I still needed to learn about the Army. I had pleased him and the others there so much. They sent me for Parachute selection training with a specialist unit who were responsible for scouting and sniper work. I didn't fully understand what that was, but I was so keen to learn.

As we entered the camp we were directed to an area well away from where lots of other men were marching up and down.

There were lots of other dogs with their handlers, most of them like me, an Alsatian, and some were smaller ones who made more noise for their size.

Bing the Para Dog (Source: Airborne Assault Museum, Duxford)

We all had our own men looking after us, and although the dogs seemed apprehensive on arrival, they were very keen to please their new handlers and soon settled down with reassuring words and cuddles.

The well-lit sign as we entered this big barbed wire compound said "RECCE PLATOON – SNIPERS". I was to learn a lot about this Platoon, which is really another name for a small group of men with special abilities in the Army.

I often heard other people call out Ken's name in an affectionate way, as if they really liked him, he was now part of this small unit, and had clearly been with them for some time before he found me.

I loved Ken to know I was happy by making small affectionate noises. I licked him at every opportunity I got; he loved it, against his stubbly unshaved chin, and often he looked into my eyes with great love and admiration. His gaze was magical, and I couldn't stop blinking in acknowledgement of my new best friend.

Ken was always dressed in funny khaki coloured clothing with shiny black hob nailed boots that made a clatter on the concrete floors as he approached. A clatter I was to recognise for all the time I spent with him in the weeks and months to come. On his head he wore a red beret covered in my hair, with a badge with wings on it which shone in the sunlight.

I know I caused him many problems, because my hair kept coming out; it was all over his uniform as well, especially after he brushed me or stroked me. I often heard a gruff man in charge telling him off in a very stern voice. He told him to get something called a smock on, if he was anywhere near me in future. A smock was camouflaged in green and brown and made out of a material that dog hair didn't stick to so easily, and lots of the men wore them here. I quickly learnt the man who was shouting all the time, was the man in charge of training.

I loved being brushed, as it made my coat shine, and the glint of the sun bounced off it, like droplets of bright light, which caught the corner of my eye on many occasions. How proud I was after a brushing, I wanted all the dogs to see I had the best coat. I noticed lots of people loved my multi coloured coat, a warm long haired patterned quilt, which must have kept all the other Alsatian dogs like me feeling cosy and snug on cold nights huddled in corners. Some dogs had short hair and they must have felt the cold days and nights more than I did.

We were all kept in things they called kennels, which were made up of small wooden houses with a small opening at the front. That was to be my home for all the time we were at this camp. These kennels were all the same size, and I filled mine easily when I curled up at night, but other smaller dogs must have been cold as the wind whistled around their tiny bodies.

My coat was so thick and long, if I did get wet it took ages for me to properly dry out, so I often nestled right at the back of my kennel, away from the open door to keep me and my blanket dry. I later came to understand what the big crow's foot symbol was that was printed on the blanket, and I saw it many times in the future. It was marked on lots of Military things, and I knew it was owned by a big place called the War Office in London. Crikey, they did own a lot of things that I saw then and later on!!

Often at night, when Ken had given me my food and water which I loved, he gave me such a lovely cuddle and said "See you in the morning Bing" and ruffled my long hair with both of his hands.

I settled down for the night, but other dogs kept me awake for most of the dark times in my little kennel, as the sound seemed to bounce off all the walls, as some yelped and barked all the time.

The kennels were so close together, all the other dogs that I came to know made noises that sometimes scared me. I think they must have been dreaming, because lots of them were pining and I think they missed their brothers and sisters, like I did.

The early mornings were the best, when Ken came in to see me and told me I was a good boy. He started brushing my coat and wiping the sleep out of my eyes. Not that there was a lot of that anyway, as I had been awake most of the night. I tried to tell him all about it in a low continuous yelp, but he didn't seem to understand my words. In time he came to know what I thought.

"Stand Still Bing" he kept telling me, but I was so excited to see him, after such a long night.

He then got my bowls and filled them with water and dog food again, scrumptious food. It was lots of different things mixed in with fresh meat. Sometimes he brought

18

me a treat from a place he called the cookhouse, and told me not to tell anyone, because he wasn't allowed to do it really. Solid meat lumps and juicy bones which I sucked on for hours and chewed on the ends until they were no more. Oh what fun that was, and what a treat.

After breakfast he would put a chain on my collar, which he held tightly in his right hand, and he took me for long walks and trots along the perimeter track of the camp, where all the other soldiers worked. They were all dressed the same in those camouflaged smocks, and they too had their dog friends with them.
Most days, I heard lots of bangs and whistles in the distance, and lots of loud engine noises that really scared me. My ears often folded down on their own to cut out all the noises and my tail went under me. The bangs got closer as we carried on walking, and then I realised what they were.

A man called out my name to get my attention, and threw things at us that made a really loud banging noise, with smoke and bits of paper flying all around. The smell of them was awful, like rotten eggs, a smell I was to recognise many times again in the future. The smell lingered in the air and in the long grass, where the object had fallen. I noticed smoke was rising from the ground, it was everywhere.

I soon learnt that the smell came from things they called thunder flashes. The men throwing them were trying to see if I was upset or frightened; they were testing my reaction to the sudden noise. Well it must have been okay because Ken kept saying "Good boy Bing" and patted me on my side in acknowledgement.

I couldn't afford to show I was frightened to anybody, as there were smaller dogs watching me closely. If they could take it, so could I. I wasn't going to show those little mites that a big dog like me was scared, so I stood my ground. Ken kept patting me firmly, which I liked, and I knew then that I was pleasing him and the man who was in charge of the training.

We did that for a big part of each day and often I was given a treat of broken biscuits that he pulled secretly from his big pouch pocket on the leg of his army trousers. I often knew when Ken had biscuits in his pocket, because my nose was just the right height to get a whiff, as I was always kept so close to him when I was in the standing or sitting positions.

There were strange men in these khaki coloured uniforms who held long sticks that went bang on occasion, which I found out later, were called rifles. They kept running off and hiding behind silly things like dustbins and walls, and they thought I wasn't looking where they had gone. But out of the corner of my eye, I had watched and when I was let off my lead, I went straight to where they had hidden. All the other dogs, like Monty, Flash and Rob were all watching to see how I got on, and barked in support as I found the man.

I loved that game, and soon they were hiding again, but I didn't get to see where they had gone. I pushed my nose to the earth, and knew that the tiny insects in the ground had been crushed by the man's big Army boots. All I had to do was to follow the scent using my nose and there he was; it was 'hide and seek'. I had vague memories of that game as a puppy, when Betty used to play it with me before I became a bigger and stronger dog.

Ken was really impressed with me and kept patting me and hugging me, they were the best days.

I was taken aside by Ken one day to a very quiet area, in a wood where there was no noise at all. It was so peaceful and well away from the camp in the middle of a big training area. It was an open grassed area with the odd hill that we had climbed together. As we approached a small wood, Ken stood absolutely rigid and watched ahead. I had heard a noise but thought Ken would deal with it and we would carry on walking. However, as I too had heard the sounds coming from the wood, I froze as well, Ken immediately reached into my favourite pocket and produced a biscuit for my efforts and patted me on the shoulder, saying "Good Boy, Good Boy Bing, you heard them too".

From that point on, every time I heard a sound in quiet locations when I was with Ken, I froze just like before. I looked at the area where I had heard the noise, and every time I did that, he gave me a biscuit for doing so. I later found out that, Ken needed me to tell him in this way, that there was somebody hiding out in front. It was all part of my training as a specialist war dog.

Soon I was being loaded into a big metal cylinder with big white stars on the sides. I had seen these things flying around in the sky above the kennels, but they had wings on them like birds on either side. I saw men getting into them and propellers going round which made lots of noise and made it windy, especially when I was to stand behind them, where the rear door was to get in. The metal ladder was really for people to climb up into the aircraft, and I found it quite hard as it was quite short and steep for my heavy body and four legs. As there were no wide steps on them, I was always loaded into the plane by being firmly carried and finally lifted through the door, or I simply jumped up.

I and the other dogs were getting braver as days went on, and I was being introduced to things that I felt were making me a tougher working dog for the Army.

Chapter 2 - Parachute Training

Our daily routine changed as we were introduced to real aircraft with all the other dogs. It was quite an adventure. The engines were started and as there were no doors on the side that we had entered through, the noise was very loud, and the wind from the engines and the smell of petrol was blowing everywhere.

The engines got louder as we started to move off. There was a steep climb to the front of the aircraft where two men sat facing forward. We trundled along the tarmac roads, round and round we went, and we all seemed to enjoy this immensely. The speed of the plane was quite slow one moment and then went quicker, but the engines roared loudly, and as I looked up at Ken's face I could see he was worried about something.

It soon became clear that we were all in a line inside the aircraft. Ken was first, and then I, and then another handler behind me and a dog called Monty. He was an Alsatian just like me, and was to become one of my closest friends. The line extended right round the aircraft so we were all evenly spaced.

Ken patted me, and then he jumped out of the open door and landed on the tarmac doing a perfect roll keeping his knees and elbows together, with his chin against his chest. He quickly jumped up and shouted to me to come. I launched out of the aircraft onto the track with the roar of the engines and the very high wind coming back from the propellers in front. I had to be careful, as the back end of the plane by the door, which they called the tail, was something you could bang into. I was okay because I was smaller, but Ken was tall, and it would have hit him if he had not rolled on the ground. I was over the moon, I

26

loved this game. It was far better than searching for people who were hiding from me.

Ken quickly took me out of the way of the rear tail of the aircraft and placed my chain onto my collar. We stood together and watched all the other handlers and their dogs jump from the open door just like us. I was so pleased that I had led the way and shown them how brave I was. They all barked with happiness and joy, as they pleased their handlers.

I watched all the dogs get a small treat which each handler found in their trouser or jacket pockets. I looked up at Ken, who was so engrossed in what the other dogs were doing that he had forgotten me, or that's what I thought. His hand launched into his trouser pocket and brought out my favourite biscuit treat. It was yummy and made me bark loud and clear to let Monty and Rob and the other dogs know I too had got a treat for my efforts.

When all the dogs had cleared the plane, we all went back to the training area, where the thunder flashes were again exploding all around us. Ken took the lead off my collar and told me to sit. I stayed absolutely still as he walked away from me, my ears pricked up waiting for that wonderful call of my name. It didn't seem to come very quickly, as he kept on walking and he never looked back at me once until he came to a halt. He turned round and faced me; this was exactly what I had been doing when I first entered training all those months ago. I had to wait and be patient.

All the other handlers did the same, but I did see one or two dogs chase after their handlers and the man in charge of training didn't like that at all as he went red in the face. He was shouting and bawling at the handlers and the dogs.

Ken was looking right at me, I could feel his eyes burning into mine, they were chucking the thunder flashes and shooting their rifles all around us, but I never moved an inch.

Ken stood absolutely still. I was poised to jump into life as soon as he called my name, and there it was "Bing, Come on boy" as he slapped his legs. I jumped up into the air like a coiled spring and made off towards him as fast as I could. I also heard Monty's handler call his name at the same time, so we set off together. I was a little faster than Monty and made it to Ken just in front of him. Ken clapped his hands with joy and I leapt into his arms for a cuddle.

Ken had his rifle over his shoulder, it was a special rifle called a Lee Enfield, which I overheard the handlers talking about one night after tea, because they all had one. This rifle had a tube on top of it called a telescopic sight which was special to all snipers.

This sight allowed them to see a long way when they put their eyes up to it. I found it all fascinating stuff and a lot to take in, at such a fast pace of life, even for me a dog!

The handlers were all in a huddle talking to the instructor in charge, who was concerned about us continually jumping out of the side door of this plane they called the Dakota. They were all worried that when we did this for real, we might get blown into the rear tail.

They decided to train us from then on, in another aircraft called the Albemarle, which had a floor hole where you could jump out more safely when you were parachuting.

That evening I saw a new sign appear on the wall of the hut which all the handlers read really carefully.

They were so proud of what had been written to all Paratroopers by Field Marshal "MONTY" Montgomery the man in charge of all the Army. How strange he had the same name as my best friend.

The sign said:

"What manner of men are these who wear the red beret? They are firstly, all volunteers and are then toughened by hard physical training. As a result they have that infectious optimism and that offensive eagerness which comes from physical well being. They have jumped from the air and by doing so have conquered fear. Their duty lies in the van of battle; they are proud of their honour and have never failed in any task. They have the highest standards in all things whether it be skills in battle or smartness in execution of all peacetime duties. They have shown themselves to be as tenacious and determined in defence as they are courageous in attack. They are in fact, men apart. Every Man an Emperor."

I replaced all the words that said "men" to dogs; which I told all the other dogs what I had done, and they all thought it was really funny.

The next morning we took off in this new aeroplane and we flew round a few times. The clouds whisked past and the wind was cold, as I looked down on the camp from above.

It was the 3rd of April 1944; the harness I had around my body and legs was to have the parachute attached to the centre of my back, it was nice and tight and a snug fit. A man on the inside of the aircraft shouted "FIT EQUIPMENT" really loudly over the noise of the wind coming through an open hatch on the floor of the plane. Ken fitted the parachute on, and I found it to be quite a weight. The man then shouted "SOUND OFF FOR EQUIPMENT CHECK" Ken replied "ONE OK, TWO OK" as he spoke for me, and this went down the line of handlers who were all sat on the floor by this time with their dogs. "8 OK" came the last reply and without delay Ken sat in the hole with me closely behind him. His feet were dangling through the hole, but being swept to the back of the plane by the strong gust of wind underneath the plane.

Then came "HOOK UP", Ken lifted the hook from under a flap on my parachute bag and attached it to a line above my head. He then clipped his own hook on the wire too.

I noticed the Red light come on and before I had gathered my thoughts, the man shouted "RED ON", with the other light coming on quickly too and he shouted" GREEN ON... GO" and out Ken went and I followed right behind him. This was a new experience, as we had done all our training from a side door of the Dakota aircraft on the ground.

I saw Ken below me looking up and shouting "Bing good lad, well done" as my motionless body was thrown from side to side by the parachute in the wind and my legs dangled helplessly.

I landed so smoothly on the grass below, and stood up; it was such fun I wanted to go again. This we did a further seven times, each time a new parachute was attached to my straps which had to be adjusted a few times after a couple of previous harder landings.

Once we had completed eight jumps, everybody was so pleased with all of the dogs. We now had achieved our PARA Wings. If we had been men we would have completed our parachute jumps and received our Red Berets as well.

We went back to the training area and I could see Ken was really pleased with my progress.

A parachuting dog (Source: Airborne Assault Museum, Duxford)

Ken didn't take his rifle off his shoulder, as there was

enough noise around already. There was a lot of rifle shots around us. They were trying to see which dogs were scared amongst us and were shy of guns and the noise. We all knew that jumping out of planes, playing hide and seek, putting up with loud bangs from both rifles and explosives, was leading up to something very special indeed.

I noticed a very important man come up to us at that point with another man who I had seen Ken talking to before. Ken saluted them both as they came closer. One was a tall man with a small moustache who smiled a lot at all the hard work Ken and the others had achieved. He had been watching the parachuting on the drop zone. Both wore the Red beret and the same cap badge as Ken.

I knew straight away, that he was the top man in charge of everybody here on camp. I later heard two Corporals talking as they fed their dogs. They called him Lieutenant Colonel Peter Luard. He was the Commanding Officer of the 13th Parachute Battalion of which Ken and I were part.

They were also saying that before the war, he had his own land where he trained gun dogs, and that he loved riding horses and fishing. He knew so much about all animals and cared greatly for all of them.

I was to see the top man once more, close up in the future, doing something he loved, riding a horse in battle. I was to meet the other officer Lieutenant Downward lots of times; during this new thing they called "Selection of Dogs" he was put in charge of our unit. I was so pleased to see Ken smiling at him and he returned that smile; Ken saluted them both in complete respect, as they left the training area.

We returned to our kennels for the last time. Ken and the other handlers took all our blankets over to one of the aircraft remains. It had no wings or wheels on it and was lying on the ground near the training area. I had been in there earlier in training before we jumped out onto the tarmac from the working one. It too had a big star on either side just before the open door, like all the other aircraft, on this big training area where we were living.

In we went; Ken found me a good sheltered spot against the side of the empty fuselage. It was dry, a little draughty, but it was to be my home for a while. We all got used to it very quickly, and were all placed in separate areas of this fuselage to keep us apart. We were all given just enough lead from our collars to be able to relax and sleep without going into another dog's area.

The reason for this was that some dogs didn't like other dog's being able to eat their food from their dog bowls or drink their water. I did see Monty try and eat another dogs leftovers as he passed by once, but his handler stopped him in the nick of time! He was always hungry.

I got to love this new home; it was painted black inside and made out of metal called aluminium. It was cold if you lay against it, even with my thick coat, and that is why we had Army blankets under us which felt really cosy once you snuggled down into them. This home, and our stay here was to lead up to the end of our "Selection", but I didn't realise what was to follow.

DAKOTA PARACHUTE TRAINING

The parachute training from the plane with the hole in the floor came to an end and we found that we had all passed that phase of our selection. We were now officially trained dogs with our wings, which were part of a group which was written on the new sign which hung above our kennel door.

"13TH PARACHUTE BATTALION SNIPER - RECONNAISANCE PLATOON".

We approached a real Dakota aircraft and the mood soon changed as men came in and sat in the seats of the plane on either side facing each other. They were dressed in their camouflaged smock jackets, with metal helmets and carrying their big packs as well. They had parachutes on their backs, with lots of straps and a big round buckle in the middle of their chests. They used to moan to each other about the weight as they got into this plane, because they had to struggle up the small ladder. Many fell into the plane in a big huddle, laughing as they stood back up.

I too was introduced to the tight strapping again which I had worn in my earlier parachute training; this went right round my body in several directions, under my legs and shoulders. My parachute was by Ken's feet, I knew it would be attached to me later on, as I had been through this so many times before in my training. The men also had longer bags strapped to their legs which held their rifles, and a bigger bag clipped onto their harness in two places at the front. I didn't have anything else to wear like they did, except this light brown coloured parachute on my back.

There was no door to close on this aircraft called the Dakota, and the inside of the plane had circular shafts of sunlight which seemed to fall through the window hatches onto my body and that felt so warm and comforting. The two engines of the plane started up and the inside became very noisy and smelly indeed, but my reassurance came when I looked up at Ken and he patted me on my head. So I settled down patiently to see what was going to happen next. I had only jumped from this plane on the ground before, so this was new and everyone wanted to see how we got on parachuting from it.

This was so exciting, and as I looked up the aircraft, I noticed all the men's faces on either side looking at me. There were two men facing forward in seats at the very front with lots of clocks in front of them, and I could see the sky through a bigger window with a bar down the middle; they were called the pilots.

The Scout/Sniper Platoon of the 13th (Lancs) Parachute Battalion with their Alsatian dogs in May 1945 at Wismar in the Baltic. Jack and Bing are second from the left (Source: Airborne Assault Museum, Duxford)

I hadn't noticed MONTY being loaded into the plane, but clearly, like me, he had found that lying down was more comfortable and we both smiled at each other in acknowledgement. The aircraft taxied along the familiar tracks that we had jumped out onto earlier in our training, and then we stopped. The engines got noisier and noisier and you couldn't hear a thing, as the plane lurched forward and went faster and faster.

Up the aircraft went into the sky and I saw the clouds go past the open door and the ground rushing away from us.

39

The plane rocked from side to side and seemed to drop down, and then suddenly a feeling of floating in my tummy as we went up. The roar of the engines was really noisy now, and I saw Ken look at me and say something; I couldn't hear what he was saying, but I knew from his look and smile he was so proud of me.

I found lying on the floor very tough as there were a lot of vibrations in this aircraft which often made me want to get up and stand. But when I did, I couldn't stand for long as the aircraft threw me one way or the other; sitting was difficult too. Ken always held me by my collar, so I knew I wasn't going to fall over. The men on either side of the plane seemed to clutch their bags strapped to their legs to keep their balance, and lay back on their parachute bags on their backs against the wall of the plane, which seemed to make them sit upright and rigid, but more content than I was.

Up the centre of the plane, right up to where the two men sat facing forward by the big window, ran a wire that was fixed to both ends of the aircraft; I was soon to be connected to that for the first time in this type of aircraft.

A man in a grey uniform who stood at the back of the plane approached the open doorway and clipped himself onto the wire above our heads. He spoke with a strange accent which I came to learn was American. He was an American Air Force Dispatcher who helped you leave the aircraft but didn't parachute. The white stars painted on the sides of these planes meant they were American too.

The fresh cold air filled the aircraft as we climbed and suddenly all the earlier smells disappeared. The cold air made many of the men as well as Ken, have tears in their eyes from the cold wind that rushed through the plane.

The American man shouted to everyone to "STAND UP" and then shouted in a louder voice "CHECK EQUIPMENT".

The men were checking all the straps and all the parachutes on their backs, and their bags were closely looked at. Each person turned around, and the other checked the bag on his back too. They were patting each other on the helmet, which Monty, Rob and I always found so funny, as we circled the legs of our handlers trying to keep out of the way.

What were they all up to? Monty looked at me as we were at the same level. On occasions the soldier's leg packs blocked my view, but I could hear Monty whining, and I knew he was enjoying all the commotion behind us.

Then Ken picked up my parachute bag which he placed on my back. I noticed almost immediately that it was fairly heavy and cumbersome, but I did after a few moments always seem to get used to it. I heard the man in charge say, "if Bing and Monty can do it without moaning so should you lot". A few comments were muttered by the men, but I couldn't hear them clearly, as they seemed to speak at very low levels and others were laughing at what was said. We felt so proud that the man thought we were brave, and all our tails wagged in agreement.

By now Monty had his bag on his back too. Ken was to be number one out of the door, and I knew instinctively, from my training I was to be number two and follow him, and so on down the aircraft.

Then the man in grey shouted the loudest I had heard him shout so far...... "HOOK UP", at that, Ken pulled out the silver hook, which he had pushed underneath my bag on my back, and into his hand. He clipped it onto that wire above our heads, and then did the same with his hook.

The man in grey then shouted "SOUND OFF FOR EQUIPMENT CHECK" and suddenly like a cascade of separate voices, each person shouted at the tops of their voices starting with my Ken, "ONE OK" he said as he was tugging his hook on the line above my head, "TWO OK" moving my hook around on the wire, then the handler behind me shouted "THREE OK" and then "FOUR OK" pulling at Monty's hook, and this went on right up to the two men in the front, and then back down the other side and finished at the last man opposite us, where Ken and I were sat by the door, "24 OK" and the man in grey then shouted out loudly "24 All OK".

We were all standing by this time, the men holding their strap that went up to their own hooks clipped onto the wire, and were all facing me and Ken. Of course I could see this, but Ken was concentrating so much on the view out of the open door and looking forward. The ground was rushing by so fast but I could see houses clearly and the odd person in the fields below, they looked so small. The clouds rushed by like cotton wool, white and fluffy, but gone in seconds. This was a different aircraft than I was used to. The orders were all so formal now as my training got better with a full plane of soldiers and dogs and a side door to jump out of. The shout came

"PREPARE FOR ACTION" as everybody converged on us at the door by shuffling their heavy leg bags along the floor.

The noise level then changed at the same time as the red light above Ken's head came on and the man shouted "RED ON" and the light next to it then turned green and he shouted "GREEN ON ...GO". The engines throttled back. All of a sudden Ken moved me towards the door behind him by pulling my strap from my bag on my back and the man in grey moved to the opposite side of the door as quick as a flash.

I didn't know what Ken wanted me to do as the plane lurched, so I pushed down on my front legs which stopped him pulling me by the strap; they were like my brakes. I looked up at him, but all I could see was Ken trying to move me forward.

I wasn't going anywhere; I had never done this before from this aircraft except at slow speeds on the ground, and especially not at this height.

Yes I could run along a board about six feet off the ground, drop out of a plane through a hole in the floor but this was totally different. I spun my head to see where Monty was, and all I saw of him, was his mouth opened wide and his tongue dangling, panting with excitement. He was probably laughing at me, but he too was about to find out what I was going through as number two out of the door.

Eventually Ken bent down and pulled me the short distance to the edge of the door. All this happened so quickly; it was in seconds. He then walked through the open door and I followed just like in training. I heard the American man shouting "One, Two......................."

I hit the cold midday air as I exited the aircraft door. It threw me in all directions; I could feel a great tug on my back as the aircraft noise seemed to get distant. Then suddenly a sound like a big Whoomph and I slowed right down, and moved my head back and looked up to see my big white handkerchief above my head held onto my back by the parachute cords. It was so beautiful. I called it a handkerchief, because that is what it reminded me of. The plane was getting smaller and smaller as it flew away. I had achieved a successful jump from a new plane, the Dakota, and I hadn't hit the tail fin at the back on my way out of the door either.

I was floating down closer to the ground, swaying from side to side, at a slow speed. My legs were splayed out and motionless. I didn't seem to be able to shut my mouth as my tongue was wobbling about in the wind.

I then heard those reassuring words shouted at me from Ken "Good boy Bing, see you in a minute". His voice instantly calmed me as I grew closer to the grass field below. A man was shouting up from the ground, "He's OK, you concentrate on your landing". Ken was still in the air and about to hit the ground.

Then all of a sudden, a gust of wind filled my parachute, and brought me gently down onto the grass.

I was standing upright for a moment and felt so relieved that I had landed so close to Ken. But then I was toppled over and dragged along the grass, bumping up and down as I went; there was absolutely nothing I could do, as if I was being dragged by my back.

Then, my saviour Ken grabbed the white edge of the parachute and turned it into the wind so it couldn't inflate it anymore. That was fun; I wanted to do that again straight away from this new plane.

I didn't realise then, that I was to do this lots more times in the future and from this type of plane too.

I heard Monty barking, so I knew he too had landed safely, and Ken and Monty's handler were so pleased with us both that they hugged us and patted us all over.

I nuzzled Ken's trouser pocket, and he knew straight away what I wanted.........."Here you go Bing, Good Boy, well done, you deserve that". Monty looked a bit miffed, as Ken only gave me a treat, so he barked loudly at his handler, who had by now uncoupled him from his parachute, and placed a lead on his collar.

Out of his smock pocket, finally he produced a broken biscuit as Monty jumped up in excitement.

Chapter 3 - Bings' First Battle

Things happened so quickly. There was something afoot, as there were lots of meetings and large movements of vehicles and lots of planes overhead in the sky. There was a constant drone of the engines from the aircraft in the distance. This was RAF Brize Norton Camp, a flat area in the county of Oxfordshire where hundreds of aircraft were parked on the ground.

Early one morning the Sniper Platoon was called into a big building to be briefed about a huge operation that was coming up. I noticed there were lots of armed guards with their rifles patrolling around the edge of the camp wire. We were not allowed to go on our usual training area because it was outside of the wire fence.
The orders given to the guards were that NO ONE was to leave the camp under any circumstances.

There was so much going on around us now, the buzz of men shouting, vehicle engines starting at all hours and making a terrible din. The feelings and tension that Ken and the others had were felt by us all; we could see they were concerned about something, but they never really spoke about what it was. This went on for a few days, and I only left our kennel for a quick walk with Ken each day, he was so busy. It was really windy and it rained all the time.

It was several days later, when we were all awoken by the noise from our handlers entering the kennels. I was quickly ushered into a corner where Ken came over to me and placed the parachuting harness on me. I looked into his eyes and he was being rushed to complete many tasks before we learnt anymore.

All the handlers were doing the same; there was hardly any room to move in the compound where we all were. They were putting their rifles into their sleeves and attaching them to their bags, and placing lots of ammunition into their pouches and pockets of their smocks. It was clearly a quick operation we were going on. I had never been hurried like this in all the training we had had before. Rob my Collie friend seemed to take it in his stride, as he had done this so many times before. He was calm and doing exactly what his handler told him to do. His calmness passed to us all; we settled down and did as we were told.

Trucks pulled up and we all climbed aboard with all the bags and equipment. We arrived at the airfield which wasn't far away and saw all the parachutes laid out on the tarmac. There was a card on a parachute with Ken's name on it as usual, and my name "BING" next to it, and then "MONTY" saw his. It was exciting not knowing what we were to be doing.

Ken checked his parachute and mine at the same time, as we were last in the row. This I knew from my training days, meant we would be going on the plane last, placing us by the door with Ken and me jumping first and Corporal Bailey and Monty jumping next and so on. All the dogs and their handlers were on this one plane, it was packed like I had never seen before.

We left the gap up the middle so the American man who looked after us on his plane could walk up and down and check on things. He was the same man we had seen before in training on this Dakota aircraft and was always drinking coffee from a small flask he kept in the corner at the back. It was black coffee and had a beautiful aroma which made my nose twitch. It was steaming hot and just the thing to have in the cold aircraft without a door on the side. He had to be careful as he walked up the aircraft that he didn't slip over. The floor was soaking wet from us all loading into the aircraft after all the rain we had in the area in the past few days.

We were all loaded and finally Ken lifted me gently into the aircraft and sat down in the fold down seat closest to the open doorway. I lay on the floor in my harness. Ken had kept my parachute off the wet floor so it was dry when it came to fitting it to me. How thoughtful he always was.

The engine started as they had done so many times before on training and selection. We were on another adventure with this very special Sniper/Recce Platoon. The smell of smoke and fuel filled the aircraft as both engines on the Dakota aircraft burst into life and revved up and down before we moved.

Off we went, slowly travelling behind two aircraft in front of us, and two behind, along the tarmac track they called a taxiway. I never did understand that name because every time Ken and I ever used a taxi, it was a car that took us into the local town where he was so proud to show me off to people on our days off.

I remember that only too well, as the driver would never let me sit on the seat next to Ken; I always had to sit on the floor; oh well that's a dog's life I suppose.

Paratroopers inside a Dakota Aircraft (Source: Airborne Assault Museum, Duxford)

Those wonderful hot days in the town were now memories as the plane launched into the air on full power. The clouds rushed by and the plane was being chucked about a bit. Although the rain had stopped it was still very windy. I could see the other handlers didn't like being thrown around as they had all their equipment standing next to them, and they all had their parachutes on their backs making them sit upright. Lots of them had their chin straps undone or had taken off their helmets altogether for a bit of a break. All the men had put on brown and green face paint, except for one handler who hadn't done a very good job of it. He was being re-painted by another handler using these little circular tins that had the coloured sticks in, and everybody found it very amusing when they looked at his face. He had two brown eyes and a green mouth.

That would teach him to do his own properly next time. The other dogs responded to all the laughter, barking at the commotion this had made.

Through the clouds we travelled on; we must have been flying for over an hour, when we dropped down fairly low. I could see the glimmer and shine coming off the surface of the sea which divided those shiny bits from the dark bits which we were now flying over; this was dry land.

The American man had finished yet another cup of steaming coffee and stood up and shouted "STAND UP" followed by "CHECK EQUIPMENT". Ken quickly took my parachute off his leg bag where it had remained totally dry, and fixed it to my harness. It was quite heavy, so I lay back down on the floor as they all attached their rifle bags to their legs. The other handlers were tightening up their helmet straps and making sure all their ammunition in their smock pockets was not going to fall out. Ken was being thrown all over the place as it was quite windy outside. He then turned to Corporal Bailey and checked his parachute and straps on his back and then tapped him on the helmet. Corporal Bailey then did the same for Ken and patted him on the helmet too.

Then the command came "SOUND OFF FOR EQUIPMENT CHECK". Ken started the "One OK, Two OK" and on it went right down the aircraft and back down the other side of those men and dogs facing us ending opposite with "24 OK ALL OK". We were all as ready as we were going to be.

Further up the aircraft, one of the handlers had placed his own little white handkerchief under the flap of the person's parachute bag standing in front of him without him knowing. I heard him say as he slowly pulled it out "I don't know who packed your parachute but it's all coming out". The men in the aircraft erupted into lots of loud laughter. It was only a little prank that paratroopers played on each other from time to time.

Then the shout came "HOOK UP" Ken searched for my hook which he finally found under the strapping and hooked me up. Ken hooked himself onto the wire above us.
This day was to be remembered in history as D-DAY the 6th of June 1944..........................it was now nearly one o'clock in the morning.

Rob the Collie was black and white with a patch of black hair over his right eye. This made him look like he too had been covered in camouflage cream. He was built for the job and as he was a good friend of both Monty and I; we often did lots of training together as their handlers were close friends of Ken's too. He calmed us all down as we looked into his eyes; I was proud to call him my friend, he was a brave dog who had done so many brave things in battle before.

All three of us lay down on the floor once we had been checked off. The wind whistled through the aircraft in the early morning air. My pads were getting cold as we lay on the cold wet aluminium floor waiting for the next order or command. I noticed Ken looking out into the darkness down onto the French countryside which was where we were now.

Suddenly and without warning the words "PREPARE FOR ACTION" which was said by the American man in some urgency. Ken moved towards the door and I hoped he would turn and reassure me at that point, but nothing. Everybody else was shuffling behind us towards the door trying to drag their heavy bags along the floor in some form of order. Moments went by as he held onto the hooks attached to the line. His rifle and bag were huddled against him with the other arm, and he was finding it hard to remain standing.

There were lots of pretty lights coming up from the ground in our direction like broken lines; some were really close and made a loud swishing noise as they passed the aircraft. These were people shooting at us from the ground in the dark. The American cried out almost exactly the same time as the red light came on "RED ON" which we knew was nearly time to jump into the blackness.

I could see Ken was worried, he finally looked back, took his hand off the hook and patted me on the head, and smiled and said "Good boy Bing". I was reassured at that moment that no matter what I was to jump into, my best friend Ken would look after me and be close to me wherever I was.

The GREEN light illuminated as the throttle of the engines dropped and their noise was quietened for a brief moment and the shout "GREEN ON GO.....ONE, TWO". Out into the darkness Ken leapt, and I followed him as closely behind him as I could.

The awful noise of rushing air soon faded as the aircraft noise dimmed and Whoomph! My parachute opened, and I looked across and saw Ken someway below me, looking up and trying to make sure I was alright. No one was shouting up at me on this jump; it was for real. The ground seemed to rush up in the darkness with the noise of gun fire and flashes of light streaming up from the ground in our direction. I noticed I was coming down in a tree line, I saw some of those lights now coming at me. Suddenly, I thought about that, and what could happen to me, as I had never experienced this before in training. I always landed on grass or ploughed fields in training but here I was landing in amongst a bunch of trees.

I broke a few small twigs as I crashed through the branches and came to a sudden stop dangling from the top of the tree in an open space above a piece of soft grass. The Germans, who were the enemy, were shooting at me by now, but, luckily not doing a very good job of it, as their bullets broke branches nearby. I was all alone in enemy territory, dangling from a tree and being shot at as my body was silhouetted against the bright moonlit sky.

I was there for quite a long time hanging helplessly, but I was trained not to make any noise so I patiently waited for Ken as I knew he was close by. I looked down and sure enough there was Ken with his rifle out of its sleeve and his Bergen or back pack already fixed on his back; he was READY FOR ANYTHING, the Parachute

Regiments motto.

I couldn't say that though as I dangled with my paws outstretched. Before I knew it he had leant his rifle against his pack at the base of the tree and up he climbed into the branches like a schoolboy.

He pulled in the rigging lines from my parachute and grabbed hold of my straps. He then left me attached to the chute but pulled it slowly from where it was caught up in the branches and lowered me carefully on to the cold wet grass below.

I stood patiently watching as Ken climbed down, making more noise than I had when I landed in the tree in the first place.

We were reunited and Ken gave me the biggest cuddle he had for ages. He was so pleased I was OK. I was shaken but other than that a good dog waiting to do what I had been trained to do. He carefully picked up his Lee Enfield sniper rifle and we set off to a place where there was a lot of shooting directed towards us. It was a place called Bois de Bavent, where we met a couple of other soldiers, but there was no sign of Monty or Rob. We had been parachuted into France.

They were all looking at a map Ken had open, under a tiny glimpse of red light from his torch, making sure to keep the light hidden.

We had landed near to a place called Ranville, and I heard them discussing the best way to get to a river called the Orne.

Just as he said that, mortar shells landed all around us, these broke up on impact and metal pieces went in all directions and were extremely dangerous for man and dog alike.

I felt a sudden pain in my shoulder, and I yelped, I had been injured by one of these bits of flying metal pieces called shrapnel. Ken had dug me a shallow shell scrape which is a hole in the ground, but clearly it wasn't deep enough. Luckily it was only a scratch so Ken patched me up to stop the bleeding with a shell dressing he carried, which is a small bandage. I was fine, except for this brown coloured bandage wrapped around my body. I felt a twinge on several occasions after that, where the hair of my coat had matted together with the blood, but I knew Ken was keeping an eye on the bandage at all times, and would change it if I needed a new one.

As we moved forward from our position, Ken still allowed me to be up front of the patrol. I was now a little bit slower due to my shoulder injury, but I still stopped motionless and absolutely froze in my tracks, as I heard a noise up ahead.

Ken was really pleased with my actions and often remarked afterwards that I had not only saved his life, but also the men with him, who were relying on my expert training.

There turned out to be a lot of Germans waiting for us up

ahead and this one act of my bravery close to the enemy positions saved a lot of British Paratroopers' lives.

We soon met a lot of our men from the 13th Parachute Battalion and moved up inland from the River Orne.

I was used as a sniffer dog on many operations that we did in the next three months. I also carried out lots of guard dog duties with Monty and Rob when the men were tired and asleep. That was good fun, because we talked together about what we had been doing.

We would take it in turns to keep a watchful eye open in case the enemy came close. The men were all so tired now and had hardly any sleep.

They came to rely on us, and knew that when they rested, we would always look after them and keep them safe. We would bark or make a noise that all of them came to understand if we heard anything at all.

60

We arrived back in England in early September 1944. Ken thought I needed to have a bit of a rest after carrying out so much work in all the action we had seen the previous months. My wound had now healed completely, but I often felt a sharp pain as I ran, and that was never to go away. I just put up with it, as I was now a big army dog with a very important job to do.

Ken took me into quarantine at a place called Chilbolton Down near Stockport in the County of Cheshire. This meant I was kept away from other animals in case I had picked up an illness in France that would spread to other dogs in England. He was in such a rush to get back to the unit as they needed snipers all the time for special operations. He said "I'll see you soon Bing, be a good boy".

Here I was in yet another county of England and where I was to remain for six months. That was the last time I saw Ken. I felt so sad that he had left me there without a real goodbye, but that was probably due to the war. He was needed more urgently elsewhere; there was little time for goodbyes during those hectic days.

I made good progress at the animal hospital as I called it, and after a few months I received a visit from a familiar face.

As soon as I saw her I knew she had come to see me. It was Betty Fetch my owner, my tail wagged and my ears stood up and I yelped with gladness. She had travelled to see me, oh how special I felt. She could see how grown up I had become, and how well I had been trained. She cuddled and squeezed me so tightly as her tears fell to the floor.

Betty had decided that the army needed to keep me with them as I had done so much good work in such a short time. She had come to pay me a visit to let me know she still loved me. She stayed with me for hours and we went for a lovely walk together in the beautiful countryside. Betty couldn't believe how well I behaved and how easily it was to walk me with a lead.

As we got back to my kennel, she gave me a big cuddle and a big kiss, as I saw those tears in her eyes again, as she handed me to a nurse. She turned and waved goodbye.

The sadness I had felt when Ken didn't come back for me had returned as she left, I was a sad dog for weeks afterwards. My eyes constantly filled with tears and I kept going round in circles, and then laying down. Was I ever to see her again?

Bing and Betty (Source: Airborne Assault Museum, Duxford)

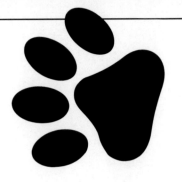

Chapter 4 - Into Germany

OPERATION VARSITY – THE RHINE CROSSING

The time came for my release from the dog hospital, and back to my old unit. I went by lorry in a warm cage. They were now based at Larkhill in the county of Wiltshire, so it was a long drive down from Stockport, to a massive training area near Larkhill called Salisbury Plains. I was greeted at the main gate by Corporal Jack Walton who was over the moon to see me. He had two stripes on his uniform just like Ken.

He opened the cage door and gave me the biggest hug I have ever had from anybody. He had heard all about me and how brave I had been and wanted to show his respect by giving me the love I had missed for so long. Jack really wanted to be with me as my new best friend, and I made it clear to him by my little signs that I did too.

For the next few weeks we got to know each other so well. He made me do all the things I had been trained for, especially my stopping when I heard a sound to indicate the enemy were nearby. I was head over heels in my love for this man, I could do no more for him, and we were a close team.

I think it was probably because I never wanted to be left alone again, crying myself to sleep each night for such a long time. I had longed for a cuddle and a true friend who loved me and took me for walks.

I made friends with lots of new dogs at this camp and some of my old friends were there to, some who I had trained with, like Monty and Rob. They had also distinguished themselves with brave acts under fire in

Normandy and survived the battle. We also knew about some of the dogs who had died there doing such brave acts to help the soldiers too.

On the morning of the 20th of March 1945 all our equipment was packed up and placed in boxes with our names on it, and loaded onto trucks. Off we went driving down long winding roads for what seemed a very long time. We stopped a couple of times so we could go to the toilet on the grassed open areas en route. There were lots and lots of planes flying above us, as I watched the other handlers gaze with amazement up at the sky.

Off we went again, jerking and braking along the winding roads, in a long line of trucks and jeeps and other military things with the War Office crows foot stamped on them. Finally we reached a big training area in the early evening. It had lots of wire and men carrying their rifles walking around the edge of the camp. A familiar sight, as we knew it was going to be a secret operation that we were about to embark upon.

The guard at the gate looked in the back and saw Monty, Rob and I and some other dogs all sat on the floor and was checking for something. He never said a word; he just shone his torch into the truck and let us through a big pole barrier that meant we were now inside a really secure camp. We were placed in temporary kennels overnight near to the billets where our handlers slept.

I knew something was happening, as Jack and the other handlers were early this particular morning. I could see a lot of commotion going on at the airfield with all the Dakota aircraft. The very same aircraft that we had jumped out of and trained on with the stars painted on the wings and the fuselage. They were being moved around and lined up one behind the other.

Cpl Walton (left) with his sniper rifle (Source: Airborne Assault Museum, Duxford)

There were hundreds of them; one thing they all had in common, was that they had no doors on where we entered. It was a chilly morning, and if we were to be parachuting again today it was going to be rather cold inside that old aluminium aircraft called a Dakota.

Jack and all the other handlers suddenly appeared from a big building looking rather happy; they aimed straight for us and greeted us all in the usual way. We had our breakfast and whilst eating noticed they were packing all our blankets into a big bag that each carried.

Jack had written his name and unit on the bag, which I guessed was so he could find it quickly if he ever lost it. Aircraft engines started up and I noticed lots of other aircraft close to ours, positioned right behind the Dakotas. They were strange and I hadn't seen many of them before. They were called Gliders and some had the white stars on the sides and others had a three coloured circle on them which meant they were British.

Not one of them had an engine, but I saw lots of things being loaded into them. There were small tanks with tracks on them called Locusts. They had tracks rather than wheels, and a gun barrel that had a small hole in the end, bigger than my paw, and longer than Jack's rifle barrel.

Jeeps were being loaded that we had used before with four wheels, which were bristling with equipment, guns and bags strapped to them.

There was so much noise all around us and the smell of fuel as the Dakotas were being given their breakfast by fuel tankers, filling them up with petrol to keep their engines fed.

All the Dakotas had a cable coming out of the back which was connected to the gliders, and I saw the planes being pulled forward slowly tightening up the cables between them. I suppose that was so no one tripped over them in the early morning light.

The date was the 24th of March 1945, which I read on Jack's big plastic covered wallet, which he kept all his maps in. He used it all the time when we used to run across the hills and he would look at the maps and know exactly where we were.

I also saw the words OPERATION VARSITY; this was new, and I could see lots of marks in different coloured ink that Jack had marked on that map.

As he fumbled in the dark, he quickly washed up my two bowls and put them in the bag too, with my blankets and spare leads. He then went out of the kennels and sat on the grass in a circle with all the other handlers, who had their rifles with them and were all passing ammunition out to each other.

The bullets gleamed in the light as they placed them in every spare pocket they had. I watched Jack to make sure he didn't put any in his trouser pocket, otherwise my biscuit treats would get broken. For some reason, the same pocket he kept his treats in, was the same one Ken also used when I was with him. Perhaps it was far too far down the leg of their trousers to be of any use for anything else.

71

They were carefully breaking open boxes that said "PLASTIC EXPLOSIVE 808" on the sides, and I knew what that was from my training days. It was used to blow up railway lines, buildings, and made a large bang and lots of noise. I watched as some of the handlers moulded it in their hands and placed it in their bags.

They washed their hands straight away after handling it because the smell from the explosive used to give us dogs a real headache, so I can imagine it did the same to our handlers. It was very dangerous stuff.

There was a lot of talk amongst the handlers about landing in water. They were loading their rifles with bullets and cleaning the barrels with cloth, and discussed what they would have to do if they accidentally did a parachute landing into a river.

The river's name was the Rhine in Germany, and they were saying that they were going to land nearby and it was on the German side. It was so wide that if they were blown off course they could land in it.

I was right; we were going to put all our expert training to good use again and finally jump into an area near a big river and capture it from the Germans so that we could end the War early, by crossing over to their side.

In life people always say, you learn something every day; Monty and I learnt something that day. After all the refresher training we had done with Jack and Corporal Bailey in the last few months, we heard the other lads call them both "Scousers".

We found out it is a name given to people who come from Liverpool and talk a little differently. Monty and I didn't find their words to be any different at all. They were the only words we recognised from our handlers. Most of the 13th Battalion spoke this way, because it was formed in Lancashire, and Liverpool is in that County. Here I go again talking about counties of England.

Lieutenant Peter Downward Recce Sniper Platoon Commander on the left with Bing lying next to him and the 13th Parachute Battalion Padre, Captain Foy (Source: Airborne Assault Museum, Duxford)

I sat next to Monty and Rob for a few hours still attached to our leads with our handlers holding us and cuddling us as we all lay on the grass waiting for who knows what. Jack kept a ball in his pocket for such times as this, and I loved to go and retrieve it every time he threw it. What a good game, but I always needed to drink lots of water afterwards.

I didn't realise until I spoke to Rob, that he was missing his old job on the farm, herding the sheep and running around all the open countryside where he came from.

Our jobs now were totally different from all of that; we were trained now for use in the Army, to spot and smell any movement of the enemy or find people hiding in buildings and woods.

We could sniff out anything, the three of us; we were the best dogs they had and we had already proved our worth in France.

We often heard the man in charge, Lieutenant Downward say we were the best dogs he had ever seen trained.

All the handlers were making final changes to their helmets and the chin straps that held them on to their heads. Some were pulling a piece of string with a weight on the end, through their rifle barrels, and others were putting oil on their weapons to keep them clean.

They also loaded small black metal boxes called magazines onto their rifles with bullets in them, and put spare ones in their chest pouches and smock pockets.

All this commotion so early in the morning, I would normally still be asleep now, as my thoughts were suddenly interrupted by the shout "MOUNT UP".
Jack and the others carefully picked up their bags with

their names on and also their parachutes. Jack was helped to put his on and did up all the straps until they had all clicked into the circular thing on his chest, and then Jack helped the others do the same.

His rifle was slid carefully into his long bag making sure not to damage the telescopic sight, which he then tightened against his bag that was to be strapped to his leg. All the other men in our unit followed his lead and did the same. As we lined up to enter our aircraft through the open door, we were the last to get on.

It was a struggle for Jack and the others because they had to lift all their kit and also our parachutes too. I now knew why we were last. We were to be jumping first just like all the times before and Monty, Rob and their handlers were behind us.

How happy I was that all this experience was going to be used again. We entered the open door. The American soldier was there again helping all of us to be able to sit or lie down comfortably. He needed a narrow passage up the centre of the aircraft as he went up to see the pilots at the front of the plane. This was always hard to do, because the men had to carry so much heavy equipment with them. As usual the American man always got his way and made a gap for himself.

Our planes were to take off first, and then planes behind us towing the gliders were coming sometime after. Lieutenant Downward, the sniper/recce unit commander, was sitting opposite me and Jack, and was talking to all of us about our jobs when we got on the ground. He was confirming small details with Corporal Bailey who was holding Monty between his legs as he sat up.

The engines burst into life and all the usual smells rushed in through the open door. The wire running down the centre of the plane started to bounce up and down with the movement of the aircraft. Off we went slowly moving down the concrete tracks towards the runway. There were white lights on the edges which I hadn't seen before or perhaps took no notice of previously.

As we slowly moved forward, I looked through the open door, just as our plane turned in a sharp circle on the runway. There were hundreds of other planes and gliders attached to them all patiently loading up equipment and men. There were just so many stars on the sides of all these planes which reflected in the early morning light.
Their engines hadn't been started yet, as they all waved and cheered at us through the open door shouting "Leave some for us". I was so proud to be looking at all of them waving at me; we were going in first, and I was the most important face they saw at the door, I barked to say thank you!

I heard the noise of an aircraft's engine in front of us get louder and louder and then get quieter, so I knew he had gone down the runway to take off. It was our turn next. All the interior lights that helped us load the plane in the dark, now went out. I looked to the front of the plane and saw the two pilots pushing forward the levers which were positioned in the centre. Our engines got louder and louder, and off we went.

The force was making me slide along the shiny metal floor and it was Jack that held me by the straps around my body. His eyes caught mine and I could see he was apprehensive and slightly scared of what was to come.

Up into the sky we went, I could see the camp below and how big it really was next to all the areas I had come to know only too well throughout my refresher training with Jack.

When would we be back there I thought to myself. All the things we felt so close to, the woods, the sandy tracks, and training areas, and of course the lovely food we were given.

The time went flashing by; I was thinking of all my adventures in France and other places I had been.

Thinking about the friends I had made in the Army, but more about the person I missed the most, Betty.

My thought pattern was interrupted by the American man shouting, "STAND UP" and "CHECK EQUIPMENT". Here we go again I thought looking at Monty and Rob. We had seen these men become experts with the camouflage cream on their faces, necks and hands, and all the bits of foliage and grass they had sewn into their jackets now, so they could crawl in the grass without being seen. They were all very professional Paratroopers, who were specialist snipers and scouts.

Jack placed the parachute on my back, and I seemed for once not to notice the weight; I was a lot stronger. He tightened up the straps and checked the hook and static line. He then, like so many times before, carried out the process of checking each other's equipment and then patting each other on the helmet. It still makes me laugh even now. The next command was "SOUND OFF FOR EQUIPMENT CHECK" and all the numbers shouted clearly back to the man, and then finally "HOOK UP"; all the men lifted their hooks up to the wire above us and then turned to us and repeated the same things with us, which we had done so many times in the past and there we all stood.

It felt exactly the same as past operations I had been involved with. Perhaps I was becoming a little bit used to all this regimented fuss around me. Then came "PREPARE FOR ACTION" shouted down the aircraft as the American checked his line around his waist. If he fell out of the door this would be his only saviour. We all moved towards the door with Jack holding, as he always did, the edge of the open doorway. On went the red light; "RED ON" shouted the American.

Jack Walton and Bing (Source: Airborne Assault Museum, Duxford)

On went the green light "GREEN ON GO "and out Jack jumped with me closely behind him, into the emptiness once more. We landed closer together than at any time before, which was very useful for me, as I could never do anything dragging that parachute around with me, and I couldn't take it off myself either. It was like a long lead. Jack quickly removed the straps of the parachute harness in complete silence. What a relief to be freed from those tight straps.

I could see the outline of a barn and a farm house in the dark and Jack was also aware of its location. He quickly realised it was the Battalion RV or rendezvous, which was a term used for a gathering point. It was essential that this building was captured and cleared before the main force came in by glider. They would be a short distance behind us. I kept their thoughts in my head as we left the airfield "Leave some for us".

Jack let me off my lead, and he signalled for me to go on ahead. He did all this by hand movements, which we had both fine tuned; we were very good at knowing what each other thought without saying a word. We had to work in silence so no one heard us talking to each other. We were in an enemy held area.

He whispered "Good Boy" and off I went always in plain sight of Jack. As we moved closer, I heard Germans talking. I knew lots of our men were behind me waiting for me to signal that there was nobody in the building, but now I froze and indicated by my actions to Jack that someone was indeed there, ahead of us.

He used hand signals to the other paratroopers who all hit the deck and waited. He came forward to keep me in view. I slowly entered the farm yard and was suddenly confronted by another Alsatian. Who was he? I didn't recognise him. He was a German, an enemy dog. He silently walked up to me, sniffing me and trying to say hello in a strange language. I turned and ran, as I was as surprised to see him as he was to see me.

What I didn't realise was, he was right behind me and wanted to play. I could tell he wasn't a working war dog; he was a companion of a German soldier and didn't seem to understand the seriousness of my work. I was glad someone grabbed hold of him because I had a job to do and I didn't want to be pestered by him. It was one of the Sniper Platoon who grabbed the german dog as he spoke good german, he told the dog to sit and be quiet which he did instantly. My first prisoner of war I thought, how brave was that, and brought back to our lines. I had captured him.

I moved forward again with Jack, and then I saw him move the men forward with Lieutenant Downward using only hand signals. The building was quickly surrounded.

As we were getting that sorted, I saw Lieutenant Colonel Peter Luard, the Commanding Officer of our unit, suddenly appear riding a horse with no saddle, which I had noticed in the field nearby earlier. He must have landed near it and decided to ride it into battle rather than walk; that made me chuckle.

He bawled to Lieutenant Downward, which broke the eerie silence, "Secure the farm and barn at all costs". That was done in minutes. We found german troops there, and also a small alsatian, carrying pigeons in containers strapped on either side of him. There were also pigeons in boxes. The Germans tied messages to their feet, which they then delivered to where they had come from. This was used when telephone lines could not be installed in battle areas and was a clever way to use the dogs. We never got trained to do that, because that was too simple. We could do that in our sleep, we were highly trained parachuting war dogs.

The tired men were just about to enter the barn with some german prisoners when I looked skywards. The gliders started landing in the fields in and around the farm buildings. Most managed to land in open fields, but I could see a glider was coming straight for us at the barn, so I barked really loudly to warn everyone what I had seen, and luckily my bark made them run for their lives as the glider crashed into the barn.

The pilot and co pilot were sadly killed, but we saw the whole building collapse on top of the glider. When the dust had settled we heard an engine start inside the glider itself under all the rubble of the barn. This was quite strange, as gliders had no engines.

Through the rubble came a Locust light weight tank with a bent barrel. It had survived the crash and was now coming out of the broken hull of the glider looking the worse for wear. It was covered in bricks and dust and suddenly the hatch on top opened and an officer popped up, and leant out asking Lieutenant Downward which way the enemy had gone. He pointed in the general direction and off the tank sped.

It was an amazing sight. First to see the Commanding Officer on a horse in the midst of battle with no saddle on it, and then a tank to come out of the glider with half a farmhouse on it. This was a story that was to become a legend of the 13th Parachute Battalion during this operation.

A Locust Tank exits a Hamilcar Glider (Source: Airborne Assault Museum, Duxford)

Whilst we were at this farmhouse Jack put my lead back on, and we became an inseparable team. The shooting had now died down as we saw the commanding officer with his love of the countryside speak to the German farmer who owned the farm. Within minutes, men were coming to him from all directions and each was holding a bucket.

They were all ushered into the cow sheds not knowing what they were about to do. A quick demonstration was given to show the men how to milk a cow. This was done because the commanding officer Lieutenant Colonel Luard could see with his vast farming experience that these poor cows should have been milked 24 hours

83

earlier and had not been relieved of their milk due to the germans taking over the farm.

We didn't keep the milk, but it did show the compassion with which Colonel Luard thought about all animals wherever they were.

Operation Varsity was a great success and secured the ability to move fast across the river Rhine into Germany to shorten the war, but it wasn't over just yet.

We led off towards a place called Osnabruck, where we were to be the lead battalion in the attack. The town was really hard to get into without taking casualties. We did manage to go in and assist the sniper platoon as they located troublesome german snipers who held up the attack and the clearance of this town. British tanks had by now moved up to the town and assisted greatly in clearing the enemy; luckily they didn't have bent barrels. The germans had low morale and didn't really want to fight as they knew they were outnumbered by all the paratroopers. They had probably seen us, the war dogs, and how brilliant we worked as a team with our sniper handlers.

The town was cleared eventually and then we moved forward again, further into Germany.
My coat was dirty and the shine had now become very dull and raggy, as we travelled along dusty tracks and roads, which were covered in lots of burnt out cars and farm trailers.

We seemed to be involved in various actions after that where my skills were used to keep our men safe. It was now the 6th of April 1945 and Jack allowed me to roam alongside him without a lead. It was very hot and the men of the battalion needed water desperately as their stocks were low, and there was nowhere to get any.

It was then that I used my training. I went in search of water for myself, as Jack had barely enough for himself, without giving me some of his out of his water bottle. I didn't realise that I had been gone for so long looking for water. I had been reported missing by Jack, as I had failed to hear him calling me back, because I was so far away in my search for water. I was found later by another handler as I drank water in a basin in a barn that no one else could get into. I had crawled under a 12 inch gap to find it. It wasn't water I later found out, but a drip tray from a wine barrel. I soon realised I was getting drunk, my tongue was hanging out and my eyes were glazed.....Hick. I was bundled into a jeep, laid on a blanket and off we drove. Jack met me and I looked into his eyes. I was feeling rather drunk and sorry for myself because I didn't understand why Jack was so concerned. Jack was so glad to have me back, and I knew he had forgiven me. My lead was always put on me from that day on, I had been a naughty boy, but Jack didn't mind really. The other dogs only wished they had been with me I think, to taste the wine.

On the 10th of April 1945 we all helped to tidy up an old german airfield for what we thought was to be the arrival of our own british aircraft to take us home. It was very hot now as summer approached and any shade was welcomed. Jack often brought me biscuits and fresh water which I valued. I carried out lots of guard duties around the perimeter with Jack, which reminded me of old times. When it was quiet he threw the ball for me to keep me fit. They changed their minds and we stayed in Germany because we were specialist dogs.

We advanced into the baltic states to link up with the russian army who were on our side fighting the germans. We finally got to a town called Maltow, about 15 miles to the south of the german port of Wismar and that's where we stayed for a long time. We had daily jobs searching houses for prisoners and guarding our positions.

On the 7th May 1945 we all heard that the war was officially over; everybody was so excited that the war was finally ended. We all relaxed and you could see that everyone was really happy and that was passed down to us, the dogs; we were also deserving of a big pat on the back for our work.

It wasn't long before aircraft came in and flew us all back to RAF Lyneham in Wiltshire, yet another county, and onwards back to Larkhill next to Salisbury Plains, a very familiar place indeed for me and the other dogs. We travelled in style, no harnesses, no parachutes, just lying out stretched on the floor of the plane. All the time Jack praised me for doing my job so well; he often patted and cuddled me when I was feeling low, with nothing much to do.

The other dogs felt the same, we were only used as guard dogs of the german prisoners towards the end which wasn't really what we had been trained for, but we felt we had done all we could do and more.

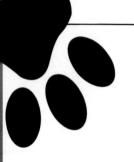

Chapter 5 - Coming Home

I knew time was now against me and the other dogs and I did wonder what the army was going to do with us all. I had survived, as had Monty and Rob, our very own camouflaged Collie.

We were with our handlers on a bright sunny day on Salisbury Plain when Lieutenant Peter Downward came and broke the news.

We were all to leave the Army and return home now that the war was over as there was no real need for us anymore.

Monty went first; he left his kennel one morning and was led up to the gates of the camp and was met there by a young couple. They opened their arms and hugged old Monty and made him feel so very welcome.

His tail wagged as the formalities were done by his handler Corporal Bailey and the papers were handed over to the new owners. We had been through many scrapes together, but there he was now looking very sad, pitiful and forlorn.

He turned and saw me and Rob sitting patiently and silently at the kennel fence. I could see he was crying, as he knew he probably would never see us again.

With a loud bark and a small whine he jumped into their car and drove off. That was the last I ever saw of Monty the alsatian dog who had been so brave and willing throughout the war. I would never forget him; he was a very special friend who left a big gap in my heart when he went.

Days went by with Jack and Rob's handler coming in to see us both and taking us out for long walks as they chatted about the war and those good friends they had lost. We heard them talk about one of the dogs being buried with its handler in Ranville cemetery as they had both been killed together in the battle.

That was the first time it had been allowed in the Army and we realised just how close they must have been.

How wonderful that summer was, but we knew that our day would come, and come it did.

The gate of the camp opened slowly as it had done so many times in the last weeks, and in entered a lady and two children. She was a young lady wearing glasses, whom Rob seemed to know instinctively. Yes, it was his original owner with her two children Basil and Heather. They had come for Rob to take him home so he could relax in surroundings that would be familiar to him after such glorious service to the Parachute Regiment and the country.

Everybody was so proud of his work. The children could not really remember Rob too well, as he left their home to join up as a Para dog when they were only small. He ran up and received the biggest hug of all as the lady wept with joy and she lifted her glasses several times to wipe away her tears.

She was told of his acts of heroism and valour on the battlefield and she was so proud. He had been one of the first dogs to receive the PDSA Dickin Medal for his actions, which he received on the 22nd of January 1945.

The PDSA Dickin Medal is the highest award an animal can receive and is like the Victoria Cross given to soldiers for outstanding bravery in war. The lady was shown his citation, a special document that explains why he was given the award. The citation read:

"Took part in landings during the North African Campaign with an infantry unit and later served with a Special Air Unit in Italy as patrol and guard on small detachments lying-up in enemy territory. His presence with these units saved many of them from discovery and subsequent capture or destruction. Rob made over 20 parachute descents."

Rob the ParaDog is awarded the PDSA Dickin Medal, 1945 (Source: Airborne Assault Museum, Duxford)

It was time for him to leave. He turned to me and barked. I knew he meant every word of his goodbye to me. My old camouflaged friend Rob was finally leaving the kennel and me here alone.

First Monty had left, then Rob, what was I to do? I found the tears rolled down from my eyes, I barked several times to make sure he heard me as he disappeared into the distance.

One cold morning a week or so later, I was waiting for Jack, but he didn't come into the kennels as usual; he had sent someone else to feed me. I didn't know who this soldier was, but he was kind and said Jack would be along soon. I could see Jack by the fence by the main gate crying into his handkerchief and blowing his nose. A couple of his friends had their arms around him and cuddled him like he had done to me so often. They were supporting him with kind words and deeds. He then, brave as a lion, started walking towards me on his own, and I knew that we were going to be parted too.

Rob, proudly wearing his PDSA Dickin Medal, at home with his family, Christmas 1945 (Source: Airborne Assault Museum, Duxford)

My eyes started to fill with tears, as he entered the empty kennel. I jumped up with my two front paws touching his chest pining at the same time; he gave me the biggest hug in the world and stayed with me for a long time. I sat in his lap on the cold floor as he spoke to me in such a low whisper, trying to reassure me that everything would be okay. He stroked me for an age.

Then a Jeep beeped its horn in the distance, and Jack had to say his last goodbyes. He was leaving the Army and going back to his own family, now the war was over,

but he could not take me with him as I found out later.
He closed the kennel door behind him and kept turning round to say goodbye with tears streaming down his cheeks. He was such a tough young man, and I had never seen him cry like this before.

I could see all his kit was in the Jeep with his army bag with his name painted on it, which had been laid across the rear. He slowly got into the passenger's side as the Jeep drove off down the long track that left the camp.

I could not see his head as it was bowed low as if he was holding his face in his hands. I never saw Jack Walton again. My loss was almost too much to bear.

Several days went past. It seemed like a lifetime, and then suddenly I saw Betty coming down the path towards the kennels.

I barked and wagged my tail. This was just the kind of happy news I needed to lift my heart from the lowest place it had reached after Jack's farewell.

She came in and said softly "Come on home now Brian, you've done your bit", and as she held me in her arms she slipped the chain around my neck and led me to her waiting car. Her tears were tears of joy; she had finally been able to get me back from the army.

Back to my old home in the countryside, and back with the family I had started life with; the love I felt that day stayed with me for the rest of my life.

Two years had passed and I often thought of the adventures I had with my old friends. One day in March 1947, Betty received a telegram and was so excited. I knew it was important, as I was given a bath and a brush. I didn't like baths much, but Betty said I had to look my best. Betty took me on the train to meet some important people who explained why I was there. I was to be awarded the PDSA Dickin Medal, like Rob had been. The man in charge read out my citation.

"This patrol dog was attached to a Parachute Battalion of the 13th batt. airborne Division. He landed in Normandy with them and, having done the requisite number of jumps, became a fully-qualified Paratrooper."

His brave and selfless acts of bravery throughout Operation Overlord D-DAY in Normandy and Operation Varsity -The Rhine Crossing saved many men's lives from sacrifice.

The man placed the medal on to my collar, as I stood to attention. It was the proudest day of my life.

On the 26th October 1955, Bing passed away peacefully in his sleep, aged 13 years.
He was buried at the PDSA Animal Cemetery in Ilford Essex on the 28th of October 1955.

Rest in Peace brave soldier and companion.

Picture: BING is awarded his PDSA Dickin Medal on the 26th of April 1947 at the P.D.S.A Headquarters in London by Air Chief Marshal Sir Frederick William Bowhill, GBE, KCB, CMG, DSO & Bar (Source: Airborne Assault Museum, Duxford)

Glossary

Albemarle: A twin engined British transport aircraft built by Armstrong Whitworth.

Alsatian: Also known as German Shepherds. The dogs are famous for their intelligence, strength and ability to obey commands given to them.

Ammunition: Also known as Bullet or Round. The .303 round was used in the Lee Enfield sniper rifle.

Camouflage: Coloured material worn by soldiers. It is made to look like the ground and the trees, normally in brown and green, so that the wearer can blend in with the surroundings.

Corporal: A rank in the British Army. A Corporal wears two stripes on the arm of his uniform.

Crow's Foot: A military symbol used on all equipment and objects to identify ownership by the War Department.

Dakota: A twin engine American transport aircraft made by Douglas Aircraft Company.

Khaki: A brown coloured material from which Army uniforms were made.

Lee Enfield Rifle: A weapon named after the manufacturer, who produced the weapon for the British Army. It could be fitted with a telescopic sight.

Lieutenant: A rank in the British Army. A Lieutenant wears two pips on the shoulders of his uniform.

Lieutenant Colonel: The rank held by a British Officer commanding a Battalion strength of troops (normally 450 -700 men) shown by a crown and one pip on the shoulders of his uniform.

Locust Tank: The name given to a Lightweight American tank. It could be transported in a Glider.

Normandy: A region of France.

Operation: A military term used for a battle.

Paratrooper: A soldier of The Parachute Regiment, trained to parachute into action.

PDSA Dickin medal: Awarded by the People's Dispensary for Sick Animals for conspicuous gallantry or devotion to duty while in military conflict. First awarded in 1943

Platoon: A small group of soldiers, normally about 30 men.

Recce: A shortened word for reconnaissance, where troops go forward to find the enemy and report where they are.

Rhine: The River Rhine which runs through Germany.

RV: A military term for rendezvous or meeting place.

Sniper: A soldier trained to fire a rifle very accurately.

Telescopic Sight: A special sight on top of the rifle to allow long distance shooting.

To learn more about The Parachute Regiment and Airborne Forces visit the living history archive at www.paradata.org.uk